CW00848394

GO NOAH GO!

For my mother Anna De Souza
who knows the King James version

J.A.

British Library Cataloguing in Publication Data

Agard, John, *1949–*
Go Noah go!
I. Title   II. Brown, Judy
813 [J]

ISBN 0-340-51419-1

Text copyright © John Agard 1990
Illustrations copyright © Judy Brown 1990

First published 1990

Published by Hodder and Stoughton Children's Books,
a division of Hodder and Stoughton Ltd,
Mill Road, Dunton Green, Sevenoaks, Kent TN13 2YA

Printed in Belgium by Proost International Book Production

All rights reserved

GO NOAH GO!

John Agard
Illustrated by **Judy Brown**

HODDER AND STOUGHTON
LONDON SYDNEY AUCKLAND TORONTO

Noah in de ark
And Mrs Noah too.
Water water everywhere
What Noah dem going do?

Noah ask Owl,
Any land in sight?
Owl say, Ask me dat question
When day turns to night.

Noah ask Giraffe,
Any sign Long-Neck?
Giraffe say,
Not one green speck.
Mrs Noah say, I pray
Dis ark don't wreck.

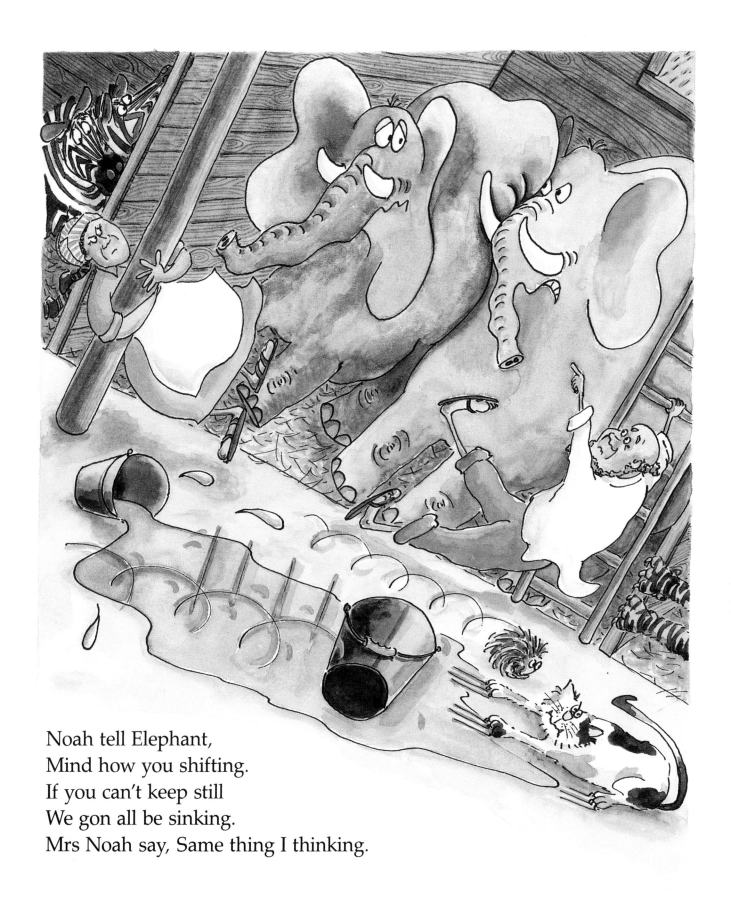

Noah tell Elephant,
Mind how you shifting.
If you can't keep still
We gon all be sinking.
Mrs Noah say, Same thing I thinking.

Noah tell Sloth,
Wake up Sleepy-Head.
Heaven pelting rain.
And you sleeping like you dead.

Noah ask Pig,
What's up Dirty-Snout?
What you so pleased about?
Pig say, After dis flood
I'll have a great roll in all dat mud.

Noah tell Donkey,
Ah see you starting to kick.
Donkey say, All dis rocking
Have me feeling sick.
Mrs Noah say, I hope dis rain ease quick.

Parrot holler,
Me think Ah see grass.
Noah say, Please God
Mek it be land at last.

Mrs Noah had to laugh
When Parrot say, Like Ah talk too fast.
Noah say, Lord when dis rain going pass?
Nearly forty days and forty nights
Not a hill in sight.

Mrs Noah tell Noah,
Better send somebody outside
To search for somewhere dry.
Goat say, Don't bother look at me.
Try somebody dat can fly.

Parrot say, No-way, No-way.
I ain't going out deh.
Ask Seagull. She too have wing.
And Seagull like plenty sea an ting.

Seagull say, I had my fill
Of stormy weather.
Right now I don't need adventure
But Raven mightn't mind a thrill.

Raven say, I'm willing.
But water high as heaven.
And though out there might be thrilling
I find dis ark is a safe haven.

Noah say, God give me faith
Or the wings of a bird.
Mrs Noah say, Wait.
Spider trying to get in a word.

Spider say, Me don't have wing
Me don't have fin.
But one ting Me can do
And dat is spin.

Spider say, I'll spin a long thread
That will slowly unwind.
And I'll sit on Dove back
If Dove don't mind.
De ark could follow behind.

Noah tell Spider,
You come up wid a good idea.
Yes Spider, lead de way.
You and Dove go right ahead.
De rest of us will follow your thread.

Noah opening de window of de ark
To let out Spider and Dove.
But dat window refusing to budge.
Mrs Noah helping to shove.

They shoved wid all their might
Till de window open wide.
With Spider on she back, Dove fly outside.
Noah wish Dove a lucky flight.
Mrs Noah tell Spider, Hold on tight.

Spider and Dove fly till at last
They spot a blade of grass.
Dove say, Look a ray of hope.
Spider say, Mind you don't buss
my Spider rope.

Meanwhile, de ark coming near
Following Spider trail.
Spider say, I feel a gentle breeze.
Dove say, I can see de trops of trees.

Soon the ark was making a stop
On a high hilltop.
Noah say, Land in sight! Land in sight!
Mrs Noah say, I can't believe it
But I think you right.

Donkey give a happy bray.
Noah drop on he knee and start to pray.
O Blessed Day, O Blessed Day.
Now I can do with a shot of rum.
But first I must thank God we didn't drown.

Mrs Noah say, Better thank Spider too
For being our guide.
And a big thank-you to Dove
For giving Spider a ride.

And to Noah's surprise
The waters start going down low.
And Spider's guiding thread
Was changed to a rainbow
Stretching across the skies.

Mrs Noah called it Spider's Bow.
Noah thought the name was good.
And all the animals nodded,
Let it be so.

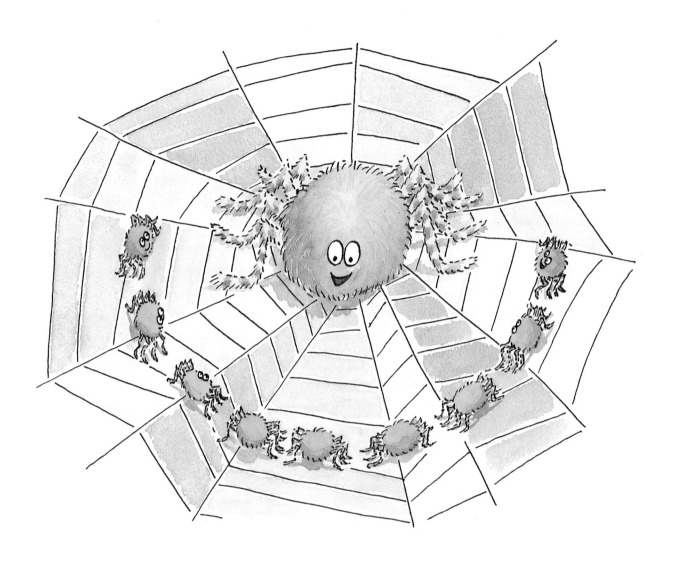

And long after the ground was dry
Spider would talk about dat day
Dove took him to the sky.